School Bus Trip

Peppa and her friends are going on a school bus trip. "Let's check you are all here," says Madame Gazelle. "Here!" cries Peppa.

Woof!

Peppa and Suzy are
already a little hungry.
"Please can we eat our lunch now?"
they ask Madame Gazelle.

The bus has arrived at the foot of the mountain. The road is very steep! "Come on bus! You can make it!" everyone cheers.

Peppa and her friends have
finally made it to the top
of the mountain.

"Look at the view!" gasps Madame Gazelle. All the children look out over the valley.

"Wow!" sighs Peppa, loudly.
"Wow! Wow! Wow!" Peppa hears
in the distance.
"What was that?" she asks quietly.
"It's your echo, Peppa!"
replies Madame Gazelle.

"An echo is the sound you hear when you speak loudly in the mountains," explains Madame Gazelle.
Grunt! Woof! Baaa! Snort!

Now it's time for a picnic lunch. Peppa loves picnics. Everyone loves picnics! Munch! Slurp! Munch! Yum! Yum!

"Where are the ducks?" asks Peppa, taking a bite of her sandwich. "They always turn up when we have picnics."